Praise for Your Marriage God's Way Conferences

"Scott LaPierre's Your Marriage God's Way Conference was a huge blessing to Northwest Bible Church in Oklahoma City. All of Scott's points were thoroughly backed up with scripture, and he included plenty of personal stories taken from his own marriage to Katie that drove his points home. He was transparent by admitting to his own personal failings, while at the same time giving us a glimpse into what a godly marriage looks like. He showed us how they, as two flawed, but solid, Christian believers, give a testimony to the world of Christ and His church. He also encouraged husbands and wives in our congregation how they may also be examples of Christ and His church to those around us. Scott was very personable and freely visited with attendees during the breaks. My only complaint is that the time flew by so quickly. I would have loved for this to be a week long. Thank you, Scott, for ministering to Oklahoma City with this much needed message."

Mike Southerland—Elder at Northwest Bible Church

"In February 2023, our church hosted Scott LaPierre's Your Marriage God's Way Conference. Scott brought God's marriage Truth to our attendees with passion, conviction and in an engaging presentation. Time went quickly. Too fast. One of our attendees texted me during the conference, "Thanks for arranging this teaching. I arrogantly thought I had heard it all before, but I'm learning A LOT." The ending Q&A session was the icing on the cake. Whether a single student or adult, an engaged couple, newlyweds or a "seasoned" married couple, this conference will be profitable for you."

Gary H. Wetherhold—Director of Counseling, Children and Families at Grace Fellowship of South Forsyth in Cumming, GA and Founder & Secretary on the Board of Directors of Gospel Partners Media, Inc.

"Scott is a speaker with a needed marriage message for couples today that is straight from God's Word. Tim and I grew in some key areas after attending one of Scott's Your Marriage God's Way Conferences and we have been married for 29 years and have participated in 32 marriage weekends. Good stuff!"

Tim and Julie Hansen—Directors of Christian Renewal Center

"As a licensed Christian marriage counselor, I am constantly looking for sound, biblical resources to recommend to my clients who are struggling in their marriages. The Your Marriage God's Way Conference is by far the best and most heart-changing marriage conference ever! Scott LaPierre teaches in a way that captivates and connects with both husbands and wives. His messages stir hearers while fostering hope and healing, and the principles taught have immediate practical application. I highly recommend Scott and his conference."

Arlene Malone—LPC, NCC–Board Certified, Founder of Marriage Center, Chesapeake, VA

Your Marriage God's Way
Conference Handout

For Couples Wanting Christ-Centered Relationships

Pastor Scott LaPierre | www.scottlapierre.org

Contents

Let me commend you for prioritizing your marriage! You have taken time out of your life to attend the Your Marriage God's Way Conference. Second to our relationship with Christ, our relationship with our spouse is the most important relationship in our life. We should invest in it so that our marriage can resemble Christ's relationship to the church. That's what this conference is—an investment of time and energy (spiritual, mental, and emotional), for your joy and God's glory.

Being not Only Hearers, but Doers

In *Your Marriage God's Way*, I wrote:

> The importance of going beyond hearing (or reading) to obeying is a regular theme in Scripture. Jesus said, "My mother and My brothers are these who hear the word of God *and do it*…If you know these things, blessed are you *if you do them*" (Luke 8:21; John 13:17). We do not learn God's Word simply for the sake of knowing it. We learn it so that we can apply it.
>
> James 1:22 urges us to "be doers of the word, and not hearers only, *deceiving yourselves*." This verse reveals a common mistake people make. They learn God's Word and believe they have done enough and fall short of applying it to their lives. Husbands and wives do this when they believe they have a marriage built on Christ simply because they know what the Bible teaches, read Christian marriage books, and attend Christian marriage conferences. But none of their learning will have any effect if they are not obeying Scripture's instructions. As believers, our responsibility goes much further than simply obtaining information. We must obey what we have learned (pages 241-242).

Attending a marriage conference can feel like drinking out of a firehose. What can you do to ensure you are not only hearing, but also obeying the teaching? Each session has accompanying discussion questions, and answering them is one of the best ways to apply what you have learned.

I am confident your investment will pay great dividends for you and your spouse. Why am I so certain? Two reasons: First, the conference material is drawn from the Bible. As the Author of marriage, God knows exactly what husbands and wives need to have healthy, joyful Christ-centered relationships as He intended.

The second reason is less spiritual and more practical. Before becoming a pastor, I was an elementary school teacher. That's when I learned how people learn. When I started preaching—telling people to open their Bibles versus telling students to open their math books—it was another form (albeit infinitely more important) of teaching. Whether I'm delivering a sermon or speaking at a conference, I do my best to provide those in attendance with handouts that have lessons and blanks to fill in.

Why do I do this? Because as you've probably already heard, people retain more information when they take notes versus only listen.[1] But did you know that retention is even better when the notes are handwritten versus typed?[2]

Maybe it's been a while since you've written much by hand. We've moved away from letters to emails and many of us rely on our computers all day. But you can be encouraged in knowing the answers and notes you write in this handout will have a much better chance of staying with you because you put them on paper. You will remember much more of the content of the conference as you cement it in your heart and mind.

An added benefit of writing your answers and notes is you will have a record you can refer to in the future. It is always exciting and humbling to see how God changes us along our journey. You will be blessed to see the ways God has grown you.

Here are some guidelines that will allow you to receive the most benefit from the *Your Marriage God's Way Conference Handout*.

Take Your Time

There is no rush. Do not hurry to answer questions, ask questions, or share your responses. Allow time for conversation and reflection. Because each session focuses on a different topic, it is best to do no more than one session per day.

Consider planning the location and atmosphere in which you will go through the discussion questions: Would it be best over a meal together, or while on a walk? Most couples find it easier to be more consistent if they choose the same time and place.

To refresh yourself with the material, consider reading the corresponding chapters of the book:

- Session 1: Consequences of The Fall for Husbands and Wives is found in chapters 1, 2, and 6.
- Session 2: Husbands, Love Your Wives is found in chapters 9 and 11.
- Session 3: Wives, Submit to Your Husbands is found in chapters 13, 14, 15, and 18.
- Session 4: How Husbands Should Treat Their Wives is found in chapters 19 and 21.
- Session 5: Wives, Respect Your Husbands is found in chapter 12.
- Session 6 (Optional): A Biblical View of Intimacy is found in chapter 20.

---

[1] S.A. Beeson, "The effect of writing after reading on college nursing students' factual knowledge and synthesis of knowledge," *Journal of Nursing Education*, 35(6), (1996), 258-263.

[2] P.A. Mueller and D.M. Oppenheimer, "The pen is mightier than the keyboard: Advantages of longhand over laptop note taking," *Psychological Science*, 25(6), (2014), 1159-1168.

Pray!

Pray as a couple when you begin and conclude your times together. (If for some reason you are not able to do the handout with your spouse, you should still pray.) When you begin, pray specifically for:

- graciousness and honesty in answering the questions
- humility in receiving your spouse's responses

When you conclude, pray specifically for:

- your spouse to be the husband or wife God wants him or her to be
- the Holy Spirit's help in applying what you have learned and making the appropriate changes

Finally, remember to thank God for the gospel that equips you to have the healthy, joyful, Christ-centered relationship He desires for you.

Embrace the Tension

As you grow together, you may be surprised to discover bumps along the way. In *Your Marriage God's Way* I wrote:

> As you work your way through this book, if you find yourself feeling frustration toward your spouse, recognize that God can use this for your good. Romans 8:28 says, "We know that all things work together for good to those who love God, to those who are the called according to His purpose." This can apply to marriage problems too. God is calling your attention to the areas in which you need to improve, and the best way to help each other grow is to be willing to ask each other tough questions (page 26).

This will be true as well as you use this handout. Whenever you experience tension, remember, God is at work strengthening the weak areas of your relationship.

Focus On the Way Your Spouse "Feels"

Many questions in the handout contain the word *feels*. This is because:

- it is not a question of whether a husband thinks he loves his wife. It is a question of whether his wife *feels* loved.
- it is not a question of whether a wife thinks she respects her husband. It is a question of whether her husband *feels* respected.

Consider these two passages from *Your Marriage God's Way*:

- "Note the emphasis here is on how a wife *feels*. A husband might insist, 'My wife is the supreme priority in my life. She is more important than anything else.' But the wife might not feel that way.

A wife's perception is her reality. It's not about what the husband thinks, but about how the wife *feels*" (page 125).

- "A wife who does [these things] will have a husband who *feels* respected" (page 137).

Focus on the way your spouse feels. Then, after learning that, make the appropriate changes that will make it possible for your spouse to feel differently. The unwise alternative is to disagree with or try to talk your husband or wife out of feeling the way he or she does. In the section titled, "Embrace the Struggle," I wrote:

> For example, a husband might say, "Outside of the Lord Himself, do you feel like you are taking second place to anything in my life?" If a wife answers that she does not feel she is the supreme priority in her husband's life, the husband should not try to talk her out of the way she feels or persuade her to see things differently.
>
> Likewise, a wife might ask her husband, "Do you feel like I respect you?" If the husband shares how she makes him feel disrespected, the wife should not argue with her husband and try to convince him he is wrong.
>
> Disagreeing with how your spouse feels could make things worse. Rather, each spouse should listen to the other, acknowledge any weaknesses that are pointed out, and try to make changes that will remedy the situation (page 26).

Similarly, if your husband or wife is hurt by something you have done, do not try to make him or her feel wrong. As you listen to your spouse's thoughts, commit to not interrupting or arguing. Do your best to thoughtfully consider your spouse's feelings. If you make a genuine effort to understand how your spouse feels, then you will better learn how to treat him or her the way he or she wants to be treated.

Crucify Your Flesh

What do I mean by flesh? Part of Galatians 5:19-21 says, "The works of the flesh are evident, which are…hatred, contentions, jealousies, outbursts of wrath, selfish ambitions, dissensions…envy." As you do the discussion questions in this handout, you are going to hear answers that reveal your weaknesses, hurts you have caused, and ways you have failed (even if unintentionally). Your flesh will want to flare up, exhibit the previously mentioned works, and threaten what God wants to do in your marriage. You must crucify these responses and exercise patience and compassion. Keep these verses in mind:

- Romans 6:6—"Knowing this, that *our old man was crucified with Him, that the body of sin might be done away with*, that we should no longer be slaves of sin."[3]
- Romans 8:13—"If you live according to the flesh you will die; but if by the Spirit you *put to death the deeds of the body*, you will live."

---

[3] "Old man" and "body of sin" are synonymous for the flesh.

- Galatians 5:24—"Those who are Christ's have *crucified the flesh* with its passions and desires."

List three ways you will need to crucify your flesh:

1.

2.

3.

Stay on guard against your sinful nature tempting you to get angry. Do not let pride have victories in your marriage! Instead, humble yourself and ask for forgiveness. There are right and wrong ways to do this.

Apologize the Right Way

Conflict is part of every marriage on this side of heaven. Because fault is almost always on both sides, if we're going to experience healthy, joyful relationships, both husband and wife must apologize well. When we do, God can strengthen the weak areas of our relationships. Having this kind of heart and perspective can encourage humility and allow us to view tension in our relationships positively.

Some people—whether intentionally or unintentionally—act like they are apologizing, but their "apologies" are simply ways of making excuses and shifting blame. This only serves to increase frustration and hurt. Sincere apologies have the opposite effect—they diffuse aggression and prevent bitterness. Proverbs 15:1 says, "A soft answer turns away wrath," and there are not many softer answers than apologies made the right way. To do this, make sure you avoid two words:

- First, avoid the word *but* because it destroys apologies. When an "apology" contains this word, it is an excuse disguised as a confession:
  - "I'm sorry, but if you hadn't…"
  - "I am sorry, but this happened…"
  - "I'm sorry, but I never would've done this if not for…"
- Second, avoid the word *you*. When an "apology" contains this word, it is often a manipulative way of shifting blame and making the other person feel bad about being hurt or upset:
  - "I'm sorry you did this…"
  - "I'm sorry you're mad…"
  - "I'm sorry you are offended…"

Instead, make sure you apologize the right way, which involves two steps:

- First, say, "I am sorry for…" or "I am sorry I…" followed by confessing the offense you committed.
- Then say, "Will you please forgive me?"

The second step is important because it:

- reveals you recognize you have done something requiring forgiveness
- shows you are not minimizing your actions
- engages the other person and requires a response

Although Saul was the king of Israel, a more appropriate title for him would have been the King of Excuses. Do not be like him! Read 1 Samuel 13:1-14 and 15:1-29. What was wrong with Saul's "apologies"? What excuses did he make? Who did he blame? Provide three examples:

1.

2.

3.

The Negative Consequences of Failing to Apologize Well

A sincere apology can diffuse aggression, while an insincere apology that shifts blame or makes excuses will increase frustration and hurt. Hebrews 12:14-15 says, "Pursue peace with all people...looking carefully lest anyone fall short of the grace of God; lest any root of bitterness springing up cause trouble, and by this many become defiled." Some couples who have been married for years have become more like roommates than people in love. They have built-up resentment toward each other from hurts that have been piled on top of other hurts. Often this is because they have let pride and stubbornness prevent them from apologizing well and taking responsibility for their actions. Their marriages have suffered terribly as a result. Don't let this happen to you. Apologize the right way. And when your spouse apologizes to you, forgive the right way as well!

Forgive the Right Way

If your spouse asks for forgiveness and you say, "I forgive you," you are obligated to do your best to forgive the way God forgives. God does not forget our sins, but He does choose not to remember them:

- Isaiah 43:25—"I will not remember your sins."
- Jeremiah 31:34—"I will forgive their iniquity, and their sin I will remember no more."
- Hebrews 8:12 and 10:17—"Their sins and lawless deeds I will remember no more."

We cannot cause ourselves to forget offenses that have been committed against us, but we can strive to be like God and choose not to remember them. When we say, "I forgive you," we are committing to do our best not to

- think about our spouse's sin

- hold the sin against our spouse
- bring up the offense in the future

There will be times when you don't want to forgive your spouse. You may feel like he or she doesn't deserve it. You know what? You're right. He or she doesn't deserve it. But you know what else? You don't deserve to be forgiven either, not just by your spouse, but by God Himself. You are forgiven, though, because of what Jesus has done for you. And because Jesus has forgiven you, you should forgive your spouse. This isn't merely my opinion. Consider these two verses:

- Ephesians 4:32—"Be kind to one another, tenderhearted, forgiving one another, even as God in Christ forgave you."
- Colossians 3:13—"Bearing with one another, and forgiving one another, if anyone has a complaint against another; even as Christ forgave you, so you also must do."

Why are we expected to be tenderhearted, forgiving, and patient with each other? Simply put, because of Christ! It is important to draw on this truth as you continue through the handout. When you don't want to forgive your spouse, remember what Christ has done for you. You aren't forgiving your spouse because of your spouse. You are forgiving your spouse because of Jesus.

You are taking steps to have Jesus's teaching serve as the foundation for your marriage. I hope this excites you because Jesus said:

> "Whoever hears these sayings of Mine, and does them, I will liken him to a wise man who built his house on the rock: and the rain descended, the floods came, and the winds blew and beat on that house; and it did not fall, for it was founded on the rock" (Matthew 7:24-25).

You should be confident that your marriage will survive the storms of life because you are wisely striving to build on the rock.

I have been praying for you, will continue to, and, if you have any specific requests for me, please let me know. I would love to hear from you and how God is strengthening your marriage.

Your brother in Christ,
Scott LaPierre

Lesson 1: As we begin, make the decision to:

- (Part I) Focus on _____ _____ more than your spouse's.

- (Part II) Turn your frustrations _____ _____.

- (Part III) Recognize your marriage is a reflection of your _____

with _____.

Lesson 2: God created headship before _____ _____ (Genesis 2:16-17).

Lesson 3: Wives are tempted to:

- (Part I) _____ their husbands (Genesis 3:16 cf. 4:7).

- (Part II) _____ their husbands (Proverbs 19:13b, 21:9, 19, 25:24, 27:15–16).

Lesson 4: Husbands are tempted to:

- (Part I) Be _____ (Genesis 3:16).

- (Part II) _____ their wives (Colossians 3:19; Genesis 3:16).

- (Part III) Be _____ (Genesis 3:17).

Lesson 5: Trust _____ _____ to reverse the effects of The Fall in your marriage.

Discussion Questions

Husband asks wife:

- Do you feel like I am stubborn?
- Do you feel like I am harsh or authoritarian with you?
- Do you feel like I am passive?

Wife asks husband:

- Do you feel like I try to control you?
- Do you feel like I nag you?
- Do you feel like I stir you up for good…or evil?

Notes

Lesson 1: Husbands love their wives by _____ them with the _____ (Ephesians 5:26; John 15:3, 17:17).

Lesson 2: Husbands love their wives by setting the _____ for _____ in the home.

Lesson 3: Husbands get the wives they _____ for _____ (Ephesians 5:27; Galatians 5:19–23, 6:7).

Lesson 4: Husbands love their wives by _____ as _____ about them as they are about themselves (Ephesians 5:28–29; Genesis 2:23–24).

Lesson 5: (Part I) Wives must feel like the _____ _____, (Part II) which can take _____ _____ things from the husband's life (Ephesians 5:31; Matthew 5:29, 18:9).

Lesson 6: Think of how Jesus loved _____ _____ (Matthew 13:44–46; Romans 3:11; Hebrews 12:2).

Discussion Questions

Husband asks wife:

- Do you feel like I love you? What do I do that makes you feel loved? What do I do that makes you feel unloved?
- Do you feel like I take care of you as well as I take care of myself?
- Do you feel like the supreme relationship in my life?

Wife asks husband:

- What do I do that makes it easy to love me? What do I do that makes it hard to love me?
- Do we have anything in our home that should be removed because it is threatening our holiness?
- What fruit of the Spirit or works of the flesh do you see in me that characterize my life?

Notes

Lesson 1: Submission is _____ (Ephesians 5:23; 1 Corinthians 11:3).

Lesson 2: Submission is not:

- (Part I) Done _____ and _____.

- (Part II) A matter of _____ (John 6:38; Matthew 26:39).

Lesson 3: Submission means:

- (Part I) A wife puts her husband in a _____ to _____.

- (Part II) A wife _____ her husband even though she disagrees with him.

- (Part III) A wife _____ _____ (1 Peter 3:5–6).

- (Part IV) A wife keeps her strength _____ _____.

Lesson 4: (Part I) Husbands _____ _____ when they're wrong (Part II) and wives

shouldn't say, "__ _____ _____ ____!"

Discussion Questions

Husband asks wife:

- How do I make it hard for you to submit to me?
- How do I make it easier for you to submit to me?
- Do you feel like I listen to your thoughts when it comes to making decisions?
- Do you feel like I admit when I'm wrong, or do I make excuses and shift blame?

Wife asks husband:

- Do you feel like I submit, "kicking and screaming"?
- Do you feel like I put you in a position to lead?
- Do you feel like I take control of situations or decisions that should be left to you?
- Do you feel like I say, "I told you so!"?

Notes

Lesson 1: Remember listening is _____ _____ (Matthew 7:24-27; Luke 8:21; John 13:17; James 1:22, 4:17).

Lesson 2: Husbands treat their wives well by:

- (Part I) _____ them (1 Peter 3:7a).

- (Part II) _____ them (1 Peter 3:7b).

- (Part III) Recognizing they're the _____ _____ (1 Peter 3:7c).

- (Part IV) Keeping their prayers from being "_____ _____" (1 Peter 3:7d; Matthew 7:19; Luke 13:7).

Lesson 3: Husbands mistreat their wives by:

- (Part I) Responding in _____ (Genesis 30:1–2).

- (Part II) Responding in _____ (1 Samuel 1:6–8; Proverbs 25:20).

Discussion Questions

Husband asks wife:

- Do you feel like I strive to learn about you and understand you?
- Do you feel like I honor you for your femininity?
- Do you feel like I make your submission easier by being a spiritual man?
- Do you feel like I respond to you in anger or pride?

Wife asks husband:

- Do you feel like I try to be a consistent wife so it's easier to understand me?
- Do you feel like I strive to be feminine?
- Thinking about the account with Rachel and Jacob, do you feel like I:
    - Act melodramatically like she did?
    - Take my frustrations out on you?
    - Covet what other women have?

Notes

Lesson 1: Husbands must feel like their wives _____ _____ (Ephesians 5:33; Proverbs 31:11–12, 23).

Lesson 2: Wives can _____ their husbands without _____ them (1 Samuel 18:20; 1 Peter 3:5; 2 Samuel 6:16, 20–22).

Lesson 3: Disrespect can _____ a husband's _____ toward his wife (2 Samuel 6:23, 3:12-13).

Lesson 4: Husbands can make respecting _____ _____.

Lesson 5: Wives respect their husbands by making their _____

_____ easier.

Discussion Questions

Husband asks wife:

- Do you feel like my feelings toward you have changed in a positive way from you respecting me, or in a negative way from you disrespecting me?
- What do I do that makes it easier for you to respect me?
- What do I do that makes it harder for you to respect me?
- Do you feel like I withhold affection from you like David did with Michal?

Wife asks husband:

- Do you feel like I respect you?
- What do I do that makes you feel respected?
- What do I do that makes you feel disrespected?
- Do you feel like I talk down to you like Michal did with David?

Notes

Lesson 1: Sex in marriage is:

- (Part I) _____ by God (Hebrews 13:4, Song of Solomon 5:1).

- (Part II) For _____ as much as procreation (Song of Solomon 1:2, 13, 2:3, 16, 4:5, 16, 5:1, 8:2).

- (Part III) _____ (1 Corinthians 7:1-3).

Lesson 2: Your body belongs to _____ _____ (1 Corinthians 7:4-6, 9).

Lesson 3: The most common threats to enjoyable sex are:

- (Part I) _____ attitudes.

- (Part II) _____ (Proverbs 5:18-19).

- (Part III) _____ desires.

Lesson 4: _____ to _____ the other.

Discussion Questions

Husband and wife ask each other:

- Do you feel like I recognize my body belongs to you?
- Do I desire anything sexually that makes you uncomfortable?
- Do you feel like any of the common threats to enjoyable sex apply to our relationship?
- Do you feel like there are any other threats to our sex life?
- Do you feel like I seek to please you? Why or why not?
- Is there anything I can do to better satisfy you sexually? If so, what?

Notes

About Scott LaPierre

Scott LaPierre is the teaching pastor of Woodland Christian Church in Woodland, WA, an author, and conference speaker. Scott and his wife, Katie, grew up together in McArthur, California, and they have been blessed with nine children. Scott holds an MA in Biblical Studies from Liberty University, and he is a former schoolteacher and Army officer.

You can subscribe to Scott's newsletter to follow his ministry. Please do so here:

www.scottlapierre.org/subscribe.

If you subscribe to Scott's newsletter you will receive:

- Free gifts and resources, such as videos of his conference messages and guest preaching
- Updates on his ministry, including his upcoming books, and invitations to his book launch teams
- Insights into his life and family

You can contact Scott or learn more about him at the following:

- Email: scott@scottlapierre.org
- Website: www.scottlapierre.org
- Facebook: @ScottLaPierreMinistries
- YouTube: @ScottLaPierre
- Twitter: @PastorWCC

Would You Like to Invite Scott to Speak at Your Event?

Pastor Scott frequently speaks at churches, conferences, and retreat centers. He speaks on various topics that build up believers and serve as outreaches to share Christ with the community.

For more information, including sample messages and endorsements, please visit:

https://www.scottlapierre.org/christian-speaker/.

If you would like to contact Scott for a speaking engagement, please do so: scott@scottlapierre.org.

Your Marriage God's Way:
A Biblical Guide to a Christ-Centered Relationship

Your most important earthly connection is with your spouse, and when you honor the person you married, you're also honoring God. He created marriage to be one of life's greatest gifts, and the instruction manual you need for a joyful, lasting union is found in His Word.

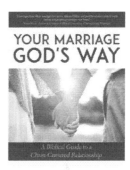

Scott LaPierre

In *Your Marriage God's Way*, author and pastor, Scott LaPierre, takes a close look at the principles for building a biblical marriage—one in which your relationship with Christ brings guidance and blessing into your relationship with your spouse. You'll gain the tools to…

- understand the unique roles and responsibilities of husbands and wives
- recognize and resolve the conflicts you face with a heart of hope and compassion
- follow God's worthy command to love and cherish your spouse unconditionally

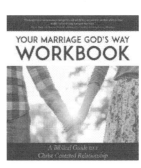

Scott LaPierre

Whether you're at the beginning of your journey or you've been on the road together for years, *Your Marriage God's Way* will provide the helpful and encouraging insights you need to experience marriage as God intends it.

Made in United States
Orlando, FL
09 December 2024

55243160R00015